The Smart Little $aver

By Matt Fuller
Illustrations m. Loys Raymer

Alex and Justin were walking home from school one day when Justin decided to stop at the candy store." I'm going to buy all the candy I can with my money," said Justin. So, he walked around the store grabbing everything that he could hold in his arms. He chose jelly beans, chocolate candy bars, licorice, and more. "Hey, Alex," he said, "look at all this candy I'm going to buy. What are you getting?" "I'm not getting anything," Alex replied. "Why not?" asked Justin with a surprised look on his face. "My mom and dad taught me that it's important to save money and that I shouldn't always spend all of the money that I have," Alex explained. "You never know when you might need money for an emergency."

"What could happen?" Justin wondered as they left the store. "I don't know," said Alex, "but every week when I earn money for helping out around the house, I put half of it into my piggy bank and I can spend the rest. I've already saved more than two hundred dollars." "Wow, that's a lot of money," Justin said. "But, just look at all of this candy! Are you sure you don't want to buy some too?"

"I can't," explained Alex. "I don't have any more money that I can spend until the day after tomorrow."

"Too bad," said Justin unwrapping a chocolate bar. "You're going to miss out on a real feast."

Alex was sad that he couldn't buy any candy.

hen Alex got home he was nearly crying. Alex's dog Buster was there to greet him, wagging his tail. "Hi, Alex," his mom said when she saw him. "Why are you so sad, Honey?" his mom wondered.

Alex told his mom that Justin and he had stopped at the candy store and Justin bought all kinds of goodies to eat. "I have lots of money in my piggy bank. Why can't I ever use it when I want to buy something?" Alex complained.

"Your dad and I have taught you that it is important to save some of your money. In case of an emergency, you might need it," Alex's mother said, "What would you do if you ever needed some money and you didn't have a piggy bank?"

"What could I ever need it for?" asked a very frustrated Alex. "Justin's parents always let him buy whatever he wants."

"I know that it's hard to understand, Alex," his mom explained, "but one day you'll see that it's a good idea to save your money. Now, why don't you and Buster go and play before dinner?"

"Okay," said Alex, even though he still didn't understand what his mom meant about an emergency. What could ever happen that would make him need to save all that money in his piggy bank

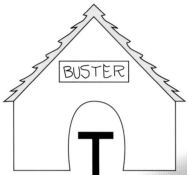

The next day, Alex and Justin decided to play after school. When they got home, Alex asked his mom if it was okay for Justin to play. "Of course it's okay, Alex," replied his mother. "In fact, I'm running to the grocery store and your dad's not home yet. Buster's outside —why don't you boys play with him until I get back and then Justin can stay for dinner."

Alex's mom left to go to the store and the boys went in the backyard to find Buster. "Buster … here Buster," Alex called to the dog. No Buster. "That's strange," thought Alex. "He must be here somewhere." They looked all over the yard and still saw no sign of the dog anywhere. "Buster!" Alex shouted again, becoming more frightened.

Just then, the boys heard something from behind Alex's garage. It was Buster. He was lying down and whining. The boys tried to get Buster to stand up, but the dog could not stand—he had a hurt leg. "What are we going to do?" asked a nervous Justin. Alex thought for a moment. His mom was not at home and his Dad was still at work. "We have to take him to see Dr. Green, the veterinarian!" shouted Alex. So, the boys lifted Buster into Alex's red wagon and ran as fast as they could down the street toward Dr. Green's office. "I hope Buster is going to be okay," Alex said, looking down at the hurt dog, "We've got to hurry!"

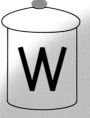**W**hen the boys arrived at the doctor's office they yelled, "Dr. Green, Dr. Green, help us! Something is wrong with Buster's leg. "Let's have a look, boys," said Dr. Green, as he began to examine the dog. Poor Buster hadn't stopped crying since Alex and Justin first found him.

"Alex, Buster is going to need a couple of shots and a splint for that sore leg," said Dr. Green. "It's going to cost about one hundred dollars, but I think he'll be okay."

"I have the money, Dr. Green!" said Alex proudly, "It's at home in my piggy bank. I've saved over two hundred dollars." "That's quite a lot of money you have saved," a very impressed Dr. Green said. "Buster will be as good as new in no time. You or your folks can bring the money to me tomorrow, if you like."

Justin waited at Dr. Green's office while Alex ran home and opened up his piggy bank. He carefully counted out one hundred dollars and put the rest back in his bank. For the first time, Alex started to understand exactly what his parents meant about saving money for an emergency. He left his parents a note and hurried back to get Buster.

When he got back to Dr. Green's office, the doctor had finished and Buster was once again wagging his tail even though he had a splint on one leg. Alex paid Dr. Green the one hundred dollars and said, "Thank you so much Dr. Green. You saved Buster!"

"You're welcome, Alex," said the doctor. "You should be very proud of yourself for knowing that you needed to bring Buster here right away and for being such a smart little saver that you had money when you really needed it."

Alex and Justin loaded Buster back into the wagon

and headed home. Alex's parents were waiting for them in front

of the house. The boys told them the whole story about Buster's hurt

leg and Dr. Green helping them. "You and dad were right, mom," said Alex.

"Saving money is a very smart thing to do."

"You were smart not to spend all of your money on candy like I did. If I

needed money for something, I don't know what I would have done. I don't

even have a piggy bank, but I'm going to ask my mom and dad to help me

start learning how to save money," Justin said.

Both boys had learned a very valuable lesson about why it's

important to save money.

The
End